Premed  Kids

MICROBIOLOGY: Bacteria & Viruses

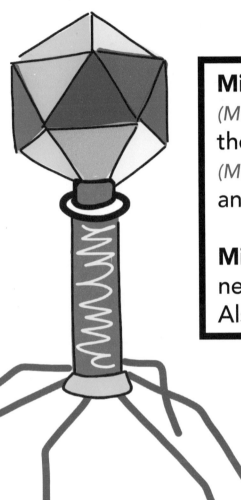

Microbiology:
(MI - KRO - BI - OL - O - JEE)
the study of **microorganisms**
(MI - KRO - OR - GAN - IS - MZ)
and their effects on living things.

Microorganism: very small thing that needs a microscope to be seen.
Also called **microbe** *(MI - KROB)*.

Premed Kids is an intro to topics covered on the MCAT, the medical school entry test!
Start learning early so you can become a doctor (which is just another awesome form of a scientist!)

You will notice references (**See "Book Title"**) throughout. These are other books in the **SUPER SCIENCE SERIES** written and illustrated by April Chloe Terrazas.
They can be found online at www.Amazon.com and www.BN.com.

Premed Kids: Microbiology - Bacteria and Viruses
April Chloe Terrazas, BS University of Texas at Austin.
Copyright © 2015 Crazy Brainz, LLC
ISBN#: 978-1-941775-27-1

Visit us on the web! www.Crazy-Brainz.com

Cover design, illustrations and text by: April Chloe Terrazas

Bacteria

Bacteria are very small, single-celled organisms
and can only be seen through a **microscope** (MI - KRO - SKOP).

Bacteria are **prokaryotes**. (PRO - KER - EE - OTS)
Prokaryotes do not have an organized nucleus or organelles.

Humans are **eukaryotes**. (U - KER - EE - OTS).
Eukaryotes have a nucleus and organelles.

Prokaryotes = no nucleus. **Eukaryotes** = nucleus.

Bacteria do not have a nucleus.
Bacteria have chromosomal (KRO - MO - SOM - AL) DNA
loose in the middle of the cell, forming the **nucleoid**.

Flagellum	= FLUH - JEL - UM
Nucleoid	= NU - KLEE - OYD
Plasmid	= PLAZ - MID
Mesosome	= MES - O - SOM
Pilus	= PIL - US
Ribosome	= RI - BO - SOM
Cell Membrane	= CEL MEM - BRAN
Capsule	= KAP - SOOL
Cell Wall	= CEL WAL

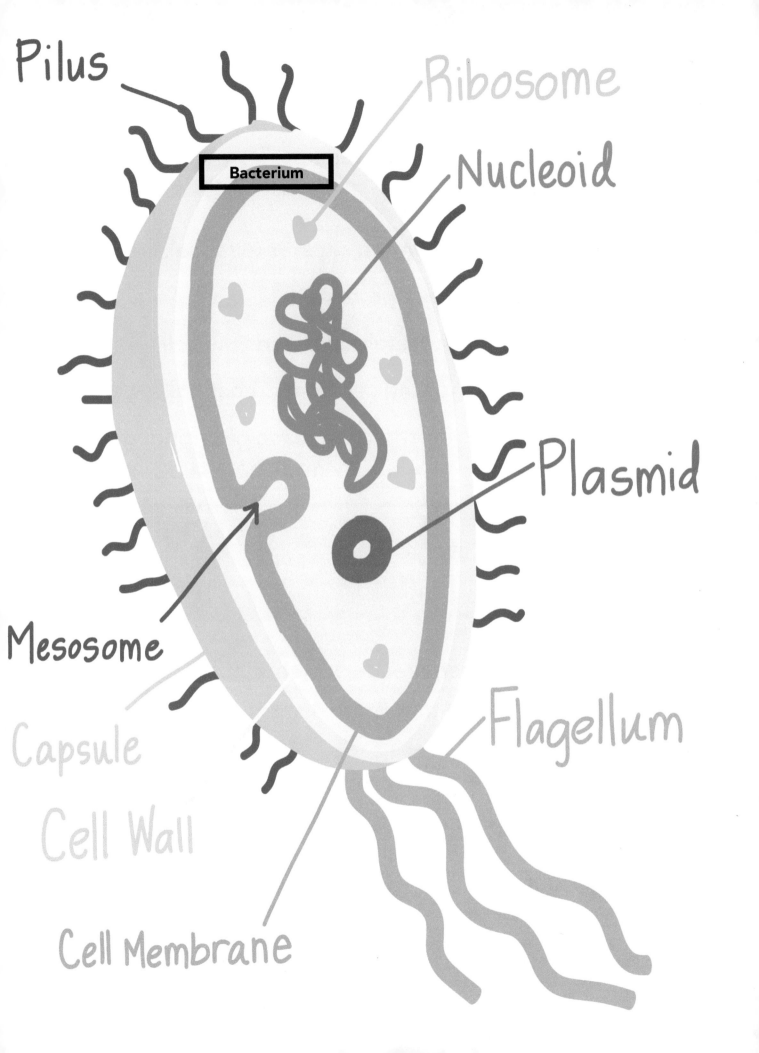

Pilus

Ribosome

Nucleoid

Bacterium

Plasmid

Mesosome

Capsule

Cell Wall

Flagellum

Cell Membrane

Flagellum = motor of the bacterium. Movement.

Nucleoid = circular molecule of chromosomal DNA.

Plasmid = small DNA molecule separate from chromosomal DNA.

Mesosome = inward bend of the cell membrane.

Pilus = hair-like structure on the exterior (outside).

Ribosome = used to make proteins.

Cell Membrane = completely surrounds the cell.

Capsule = protection for the cell from predators.

Cell Wall = tough, rigid protection made of peptidoglycan.

(PEP - TID - O - GLI - KAN)

Bacteria are in almost everything.
There are good bacteria and bad bacteria.

Bacteria are in soil, water, bread and in our bodies!
Humans have bacteria in the mouth, lungs and intestines.

Some very powerful bacteria in a cow's stomach break down
the very strong cell wall in plants, called cellulose. **(See Botany)**
This allows the cow to benefit from all of the nutrients in plants.

Bacteria can also cause illnesses like ear **infections** (IN-FEK-SHUN),
pneumonia (NU - MON - EE - UH) and strep.

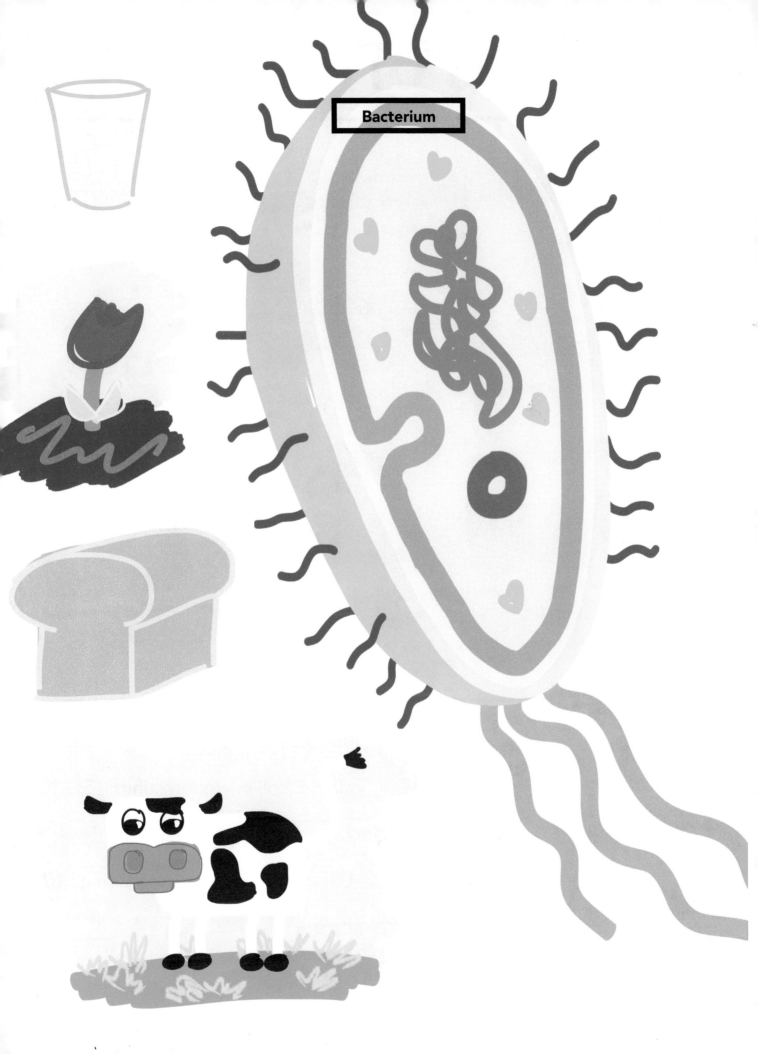

Bacterium

Types of Bacteria

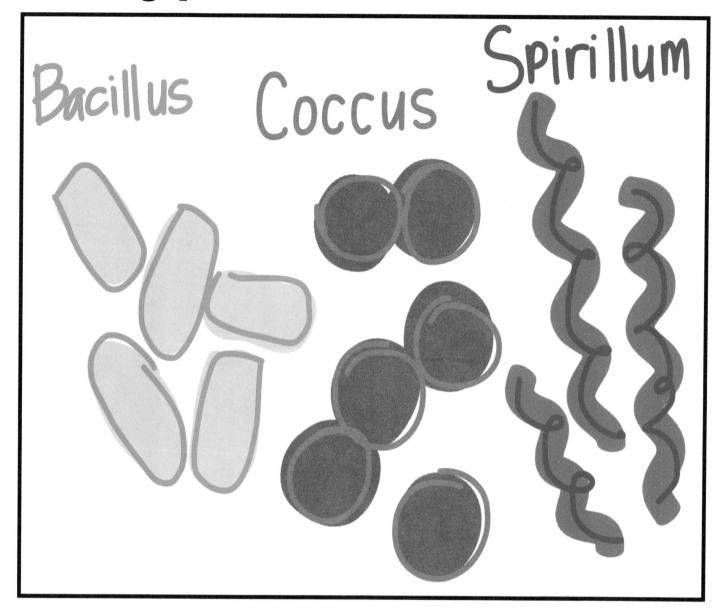

Bacillus BUH - SIL - US = rod shaped (like the previous illustration).

We have **bacillus** shaped bacteria called E.coli in our intestines. (GOOD)

Coccus KOK - US = sphere shaped.

Streptococcus (STREP - TO - KOK - US) bacteria cause strep throat. (BAD)

Spirillum SPI - RIL - LUM = spiral shaped.

Most **spirilla** bacteria live in water.

Bacteria are tiny, single-celled, **prokaryotes**.
A **prokaryote** is an organism with NO nucleus.
A **eukaryote** is an organism WITH a nucleus.

A cell of bacteria has the following parts:
Flagellum
Nucleoid
Plasmid
Mesosome
Pilus
Ribosome
Cell Membrane
Capsule
and Cell Wall

Bacteria are found throughout our body,
in bread, soil, water, almost everything!

Strong bacteria in the stomach of a cow
break down cellulose so the cow gets nutrients.

BUT, bad bacteria can cause illnesses like
ear infections, pneumonia and strep.

The three main types of bacteria are:
bacillus, **coccus** and **spirillus**.

Next, VIRUSES!

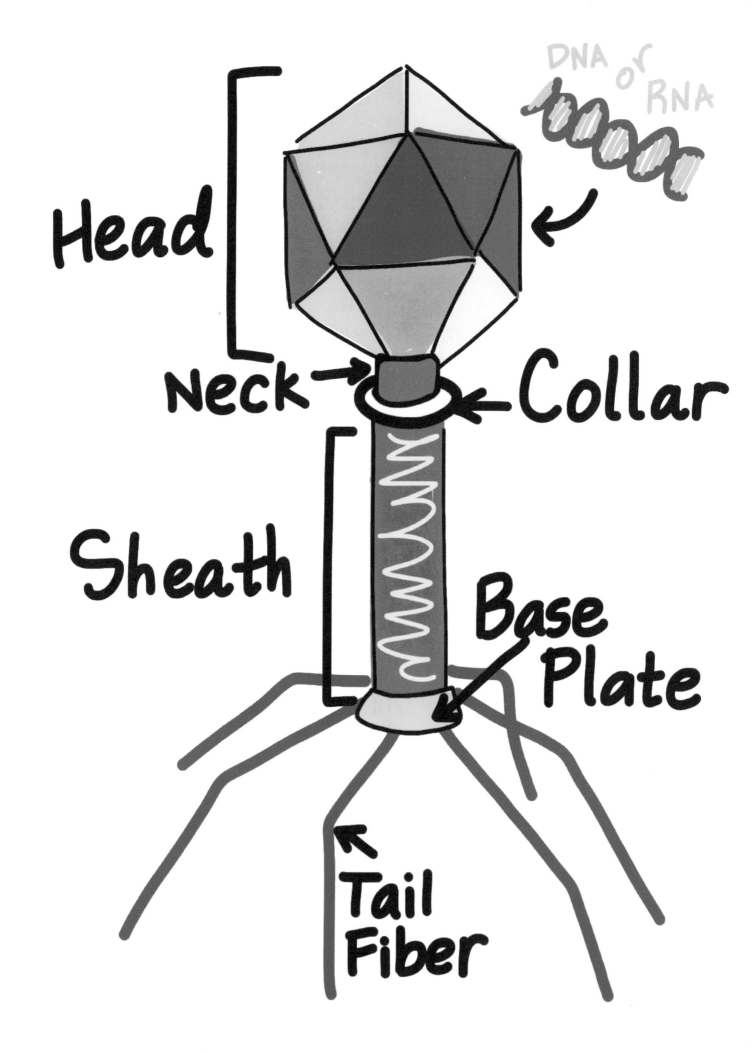

Viruses

(VI - RUSS - IS)

Viruses are teeny tiny and cause **infection**. They are so small that you cannot see them unless you are using a **microscope**. They are even smaller than bacteria!

There are different kinds of viruses.

This **virus** is a T2 **bacteriophage**. (BAK - TEER - EE - O - FAJ) **Bacteriophages** infect bacteria.

A bacteriophage is made of a Head with DNA or RNA inside, Neck, Collar, Sheath, Base Plate and Tail fibers.

The <u>head</u> is covered with a protein (PRO - TEEN) coat called a **capsid**. (KAP - SID)

DID YOU KNOW that viruses are NOT LIVING?
Viruses need a HOST (something living)
to replicate (make copies), and to get energy.
Viruses have ONLY DNA *or* ONLY RNA, but never both.

All living organisms have <u>BOTH</u> DNA *AND* RNA.

How a bacteriophage infects a bacterium

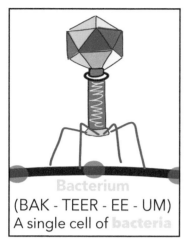

Bacterium
(BAK - TEER - EE - UM)
A single cell of bacteria

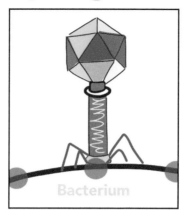

Bacterium

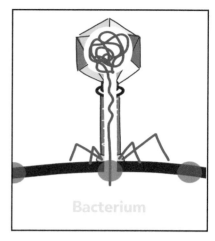

Bacterium

1. Infection by a **virus** begins with the **virus** landing on a host cell. *Bacteriophages* **infect** *bacteria*.

2. Then the **virus** attaches the base plate to a **receptor** on the host cell.

3. Next, the **nucleic acid** (NU - KLA - IK   AS - ID), is injected into the host cell. (DNA or RNA, but never both.)

After the bacteriophage has injected the host cell with **nucleic acid**, there are two potential cycles for **infection**.

Lytic Cycle (LIT - IK) and
Lysogenic Cycle (LI - SO - JEN - IK)

The Lytic Cycle always results in host cell death.
In the Lysogenic Cycle, **nucleic acid** is added to the bacterial DNA (**genome**). The host cell continues normally.
It is like the **virus** is "sleeping" because it is inactive.

However, at some point, the cell may remove the viral DNA or RNA from its DNA, causing the **virus** to become active.
It then enters the Lytic Cycle and results in host cell death.

Two types of infection by bacteriophage: LYTIC and LYSOGENIC

Lytic cycle:

(1) a normal bacterium,

(2) the **virus** lands on the host cell and attaches to a **receptor**,

(3) the **virus** injects **nucleic acid** into the host,

(4) the **virus** takes control of the host cell and uses the host cell to make copies of its **nucleic acid**,

(5) new bacteriophages are built using the new viral copies,

(6) the cell is so full of **viruses** that it will burst open, killing the host cell and releasing the **viruses** to **infect** more host cells!

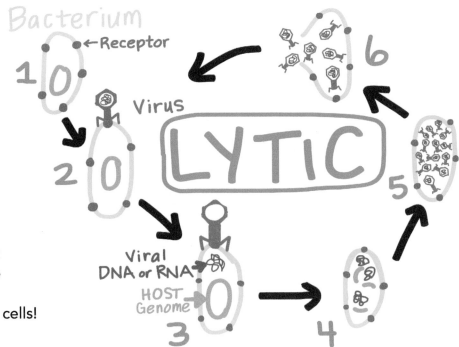

Lysogenic cycle:

(1-3 SAME AS LYTIC)

(4) the **nucleic acid** is combined with the host **genome**. (JEE - NOM)

*The **genome** is the DNA of the host.*

(5) the host replicates (makes copies) including the new **nucleic acid** that was added.

(6) the cell will continue normally and cycle back to (4), unless

(7) at some point, the host cell removes the viral **nucleic acid** from its **genome**.

The viral **nucleic acid** is now loose and the **virus** becomes active, entering the LYTIC CYCLE.

(8) = *step (4)* **Lytic**, makes copies

(9) = *step (5) and (6)* **Lytic**, bacteriophages are built, filling the cell with **viruses** to the point that the cell bursts open, releasing the **viruses**.

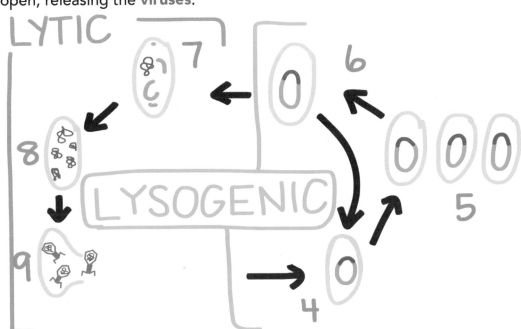

*The host cell MUST have a **receptor** for the **virus** to attach. No **receptor** means no **infection**.

Enveloped vs **non**-enveloped viruses **in humans**

Enveloped (IN - VEL - UPD) means that the **virus** has an envelope around it similar to the membrane of the host cell.
This enveloped **virus** (**Influenza**) is taken into the host cell by **endocytosis** (IN - DO - SI - TO - SIS) --- the cell eats the **virus**.

Non-enveloped viruses do not have an envelope, just a capsid. Some can also be taken in by **endocytosis**. (Adenovirus, turn page)

This is different from bacteriophages *(also **non**-enveloped)* *which land on the* bacterium *and **inject** nucleic acid.*

In enveloped and **non**-enveloped viruses, the **spikes** on the surface attach to the **receptor** on the host cell membrane, like a key going into a lock. The **virus** is brought into the host cell where the **viral RNA** is released and replicated forming new **viruses**.

Influenza virus infecting a human cell:

(1) The **spikes** on the **virus** bind with the **receptor** on the host.
(2) The **virus** is taken into the cell through **endocytosis**.
(3) A vesicle is formed around the **virus**, like a bubble.
(4) The vesicle and viral envelope come together,
    releasing **viral RNA** into the cell.
(5) Copies are made of the **viral RNA**, proteins
    and **spikes** on the outer membrane (bottom of host).
(6) New **viruses** are assembled with proteins.
(7) The new **virus** buds out of the host cell.
(8) A new **influenza virus** is released.

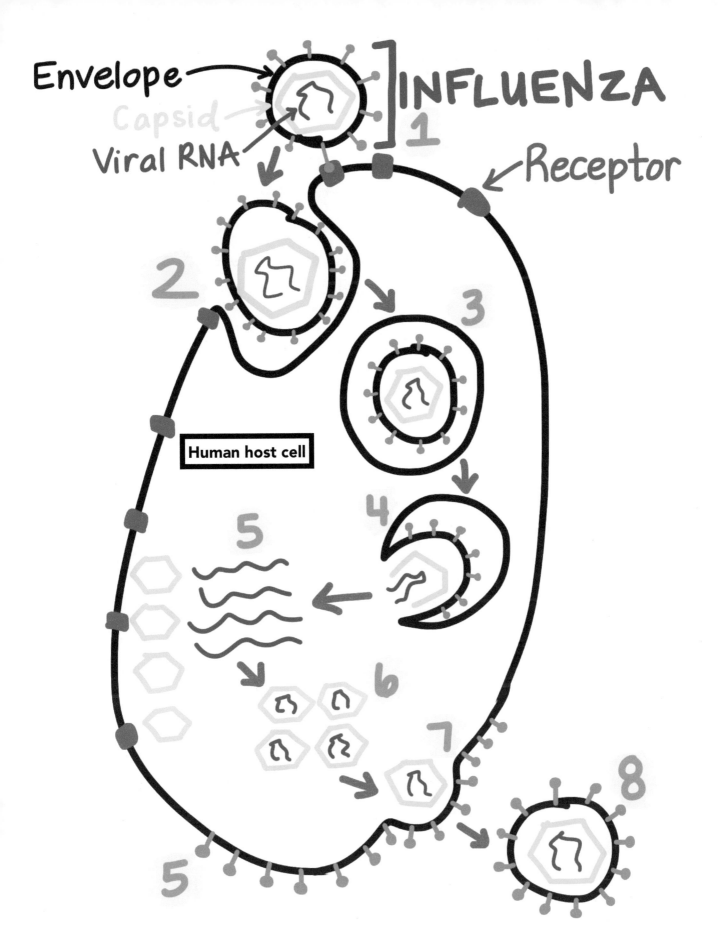

Envelope

Capsid

Viral RNA

INFLUENZA

1

Receptor

2

3

Human host cell

4

5

6

7

8

5

Our bodies fight **viruses** with the immune system.

(See Anatomy & Physiology Part 2)

Other Viruses

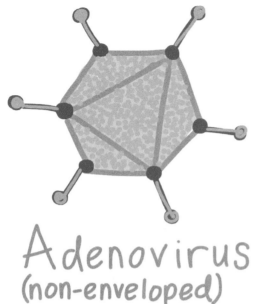

Adenovirus (UH - DEN - O - VI - RUS) causes respiratory (RES - PI - RUH - TOR - EE) infections and pink eye.

Adenovirus is a **non**-enveloped **virus** having a **capsid** instead of an envelope, like the T2 bacteriophage.

Adenovirus
(non-enveloped)

Rabies (RAY - BEEZ) comes from an animal bite and causes inflammation (IN - FLUH - MA - SHUN) in the central nervous system. **(See Neurology)**

Rabies is an enveloped **virus**.
It has an envelope, like **influenza**.

Rabies
(enveloped)

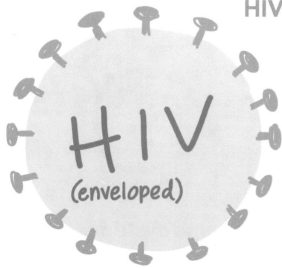

HIV
(enveloped)

HIV is a special **virus** called a **retrovirus**.
HIV uses an enzyme called
reverse transcriptase
(RE - VRS   TRANS - KRIPT - AZE)
to copy its RNA into DNA,
which it then inserts into
the host cell genome.

HIV is an enveloped **virus**,
it has an envelope.

Viruses are teeny tiny and cause **infection**.
Viruses have ONLY DNA or RNA, but never both.

A T2 bacteriophage infects bacteria by landing
on a host cell **receptor** and injecting **nucleic acid**.
The **virus** will then enter the **Lytic** or Lysogenic Cycle.
The **Lytic Cycle** kills the host cell.
The Lysogenic Cycle is when the **virus** "sleeps" until the
viral DNA or RNA is removed from the **genome**
becoming active and continuing the **Lytic Cycle**.

Viruses are either enveloped or **non**-enveloped.
Enveloped means the **virus** has an envelope membrane
surrounding it similar to the host **cell membrane**.
Influenza, **rabies** and HIV are enveloped **viruses**.

Influenza is taken into the cell by **endocytosis**.
Rabies causes inflammation of the central nervous system.
HIV is special because it is a **retrovirus**.
It has reverse transcriptase that copies its RNA into DNA,
which it then puts into the host cell **genome**.

Non-enveloped **viruses** have a capsid surrounding the
genetic material. Adenovirus is a **non**-enveloped **virus**.
Adenovirus causes respiratory infections.

Viruses have different shapes but the goal of all **viruses**
is to invade the host cell and use the host cell
to produce more **viruses**.

Bacteria QUIZ

What is the definition of **microbiology**?

What is another word for **microorganism**?

Are bacteria **prokaryotes** or **eukaryotes**?

Describe a **prokaryote** and a **eukaryote**.

Name the parts of a bacterium.

The chromosomal DNA forms the _____ in bacteria.

How does a bacterium move?

What two parts of the bacterium provide protection?

Where can bacteria be found?

Name an example of a bad bacteria.

What are the 3 types of bacteria?

Viruses QUIZ

Which is bigger, a bacterium or a **virus**?

The T2 bacteriophage infects _____ .

Name the parts of the T2 bacteriophage.

Are **viruses** alive? Why or why not?

Compare the **Lytic Cycle** to the Lysogenic Cycle.

Can a **virus** attach to a host cell without a **receptor**?

Describe an enveloped and **non**-enveloped **virus**.

Name an enveloped and **non**-enveloped **virus**.

What is **endocytosis**?

HIV is special because it has _____ _____ which copies RNA into DNA, to be inserted into the host **genome**.

What is the goal of all **viruses**?

_____

Use the following page to draw a bacterium and/or **virus**!

CPSIA information can be obtained
at www.ICGtesting.com
Printed in the USA
BVHW050711020420
576571BV00003B/74